# My Best Short Story

## in 500 words

Written by
**Christopher Edge**

Illustrated by
**Nathan Reed**

**OXFORD**
UNIVERSITY PRESS

# OXFORD
## UNIVERSITY PRESS

Oxford University Press is a department of the University of Oxford.
It furthers the University's objective of excellence in research, scholarship,
and education by publishing worldwide. Oxford is a registered trade mark of
Oxford University Press in the UK and in certain other countries

Text © Christopher Edge 2018
Database rights Oxford University Press
Illustrations © Nathan Reed
The moral rights of the author and illustrator have been asserted

First published 2018

British Library Cataloguing in Publication Data

Data available

ISBN: 978-0-19-277151-3

1 3 5 7 9 10 8 6 4 2

Printed in China

Paper used in the production of this book is a natural,
recyclable product made from wood grown in sustainable forests.
The manufacturing process conforms to the environmental
regulations of the country of origin.

## Oxford OWL

**For school**
Discover eBooks, inspirational
resources, advice and support

**For home**
Helping your child's learning
with free eBooks, essential
tips and fun activities

## www.oxfordowl.co.uk

# Contents

# The story of you

Every story has an author
and for this story it's you!

Stick a photo or draw a picture of yourself here.

# Now tell the reader a bit about yourself.

My name is... _____

I live in... _____

These are some of my favourite things... _____
_____
_____

# Have you read an amazing book?
# Do you have a favourite author?

My favourite book is... _____

My favourite author is... _____

I like stories about... _____
_____
_____

# Short story ideas

Want to write a great short story? Find an idea! Look around for an unusual object.

## A fantastic find

Draw a picture of the object here.

# Now plan your story.

Who found it?
_____
_____
_____

Where?
_____
_____
_____

What is it used for?
_____
_____
_____

Who is looking for it?
_____
_____
_____

Does it hold a secret?
_____
_____
_____

# Choose your characters

Every story needs a star. This could be a daring superhero or even a dastardly villain.

a robot

a girl

a unicorn

an alien

a boy

a mouse

## Draw your character here

# Describe your character.

My character's name is...

My character looks like...

My character is good at...

My character's greatest fear is...

Circle three words that you think best describe your character.

| | | | |
|---|---|---|---|
| helpful | scared | quiet | shy |
| kind | mean | inventive | tall |
| brave | bossy | greedy | tiny |
| brainy | clumsy | sneaky | magical |
| silly | loud | chatty | shiny |

# Set the scene

## A great story can be set anywhere.

Perhaps it might start in your school or your living room and then your character could travel to an unexpected place, like another planet, or get sucked into a video game!

## Why not choose one or more of these locations for your story?

Planet X

Underwater world

Science lab

football field

Egypt

Battle One game world

# My Map

Draw a map showing the key places in your story here. Draw a dotted line between different places to show the journey your character takes in the story.

# Fun with words

You need to pick the perfect words to tell your story. You could use a thesaurus, be creative with the words you choose or invent your own vocabulary.

## Vocabulary inventor

Blending different words together can help you to add interesting ideas and characters to your story.

bull + fox = **buffox**
hullaballoo + balloon = **hullaballoon**
beard + cardigan = **beardigan**
scamp + vampire = **scampire**

## Get blending!

_____ + _____ = _____

_____ + _____ = _____

_____ + _____ = _____

_____ + _____ = _____

# Choose your title

Now you need to create a title for your story that grabs the reader's attention.

Is your story a mystery or an adventure? You could include a word that tells the reader what kind of story it is.

Mystery          Adventure          Love          Creepy          Detective          Spy

_____

Will you name your hero or your villain in the title?

_____

How I Learned How To Tidy My Room and Accidentally Saved the Human Race

The Painted People Mystery

The Island of Forgetting

Will your title include the name of the place where your story happens?

_____

* Now pick your favourite.

# Start your story

There are lots of different ways of starting a story. Here are some opening lines to get your story going.

I looked in the mirror and saw . . .

I didn't want to go . . .

It started like a normal day . . .

'Stop!' he screamed. 'If you open that . . .

BANG! The explosion rocked the spaceship . . .

Dear diary . . .

Once upon a time . . .

# Now you have your big idea. Let's get started...

# What happens next

**Every story has a beginning, a middle and an end. A great story needs some twists and turns to keep readers glued to their seats.**

What problem does your character face? Do they need to get somewhere or find something? What obstacle might be put in their way? What can they do? How can they get help?

Fix the glitch to find your way out of the game.

Travel back in time to return Queen Elizabeth's stolen tiara.

Help the witch who has lost her wand.

# Plan the middle of your story.

Problem: My character's problem is...

_____

_____

_____

Problem solved: My character solves this by...

_____

_____

_____

Obstacle: The obstacle that gets in my character's way is...

_____

_____

_____

Obstacle overcome: My character gets past this obstacle by...

_____

_____

_____

# Now write the middle of your story.

# The End

A great story needs a great ending. Take a look at how these endings wrap the story up.

A detective dog solves the mystery of the missing bone.

A brainy kid uploads a virus to defeat a robot army.

The shyest girl in school wins the talent show.

A frightened ghost learns how to be scary.

An explorer finds the buried treasure.

A scientist shrinks the world to defeat alien invaders.

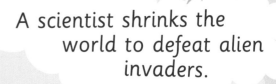

# How could you end your story?

Idea 1

Idea 2

Idea 3

Idea 4

# Now pick your favourite idea and write the rest of your story with a great ending!

_____

_____

_____

_____

_____

_____

_____

_____

_____

_____

_____

_____

_____

_____

_____

_____

_____

# Edit your story

You might have finished writing your story, but is it the best it can be?

Does it all make sense?

Did you use the best words in your descriptions?

Did you remember all the capital letters and full stops?

Have you read through your story?

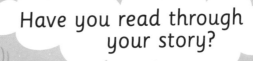

Use the **story doctor checklist** to help you make your story even more awesome. You could get a friend or family member to complete this checklist after reading your story or just fill it in yourself.

# Story doctor

Does the opening of the story grab your attention?  **Yes** ☐ **No** ☐

Say why: _____

What's your favourite part of the story? Do you have one? **Yes** ☐ **No** ☐

Say why: _____

Do you have a favourite word or phrase in the story?  **Yes** ☐ **No** ☐

Say why: _____

Did you find any parts of the story confusing?  **Yes** ☐ **No** ☐

Say why: _____

Do you like the ending?  **Yes** ☐ **No** ☐

Say why: _____

What would make the story better? Any ideas?  **Yes** ☐ **No** ☐

Say why: _____

# Design a cover

Every great story needs a great cover. From doodle-tastic drawings to artwork with the wow factor, it's time to get designing! Don't forget to include the title of the story in your design.

# Write a blurb

## A blurb is a short description that tells readers what a story is about.

Take a look at the back cover of your favourite book. Now write a blurb for your story.

When Daisy Jones found an old-fashioned key she didn't know it would unlock the greatest adventure of her life...

# My best short story!

Now it's time to bring your beginning, middle and end together as you write your best short story. Whether this is 50 or 500 words long, make sure you keep the reader hooked until the very last line.

_____

_____

_____

_____

_____

_____

_____

_____

_____

_____

## - - ✗ THE END ✗ - -

Well done! What's your next big idea?

**For more story-writing ideas see**

Age 7+

**Also available:**

Age 5+

Age 5+

Age 5+

Age 5+

**For more vocabulary see**

Age 5+

Age 5+

Age 8+

www.oxfordschooldictionaries.com